THE Elements BOOK 2

FIRE

Etna in eruption.

FIRE

BERNARD HENRY

Does not our life consist of the four elements?

SHAKESPEARE (*Twelfth Night*)

ROY PUBLICATIONS, INC.
NEW YORK 10021

The Elements Series
© 1968
John Baker Publishers Limited

FIRE
© 1968 Bernard Henry

Library of Congress Number 68-23903

Printed in Great Britain

Contents

Acknowledgments

Thanks are due for information provided by: Mr B. S. Lawrence of Bryant & May Ltd. (in addition to illustrations acknowledged below), and we must commend the value of The Bryant & May Museum of Firemaking Appliances at the Science Museum in Kensington, London, S.W.7; Mrs Sterling of the Fire Protection Association (illustrations acknowledged below), for help with certain details; the Coal Board; the Gas Council; the Electricity Council, EDA Division; the Petroleum Information Bureau.

For permission to reproduce the various illustrations; Clifford C. Ashton, no. 28; Associated Press, no. 27; The Astronomer Royal, Royal Greenwich Observatory, no. 1; Barnaby's (Mustograph), no. 14; Black Star (Sulzer), frontispiece, (Dr Georg Gerster), no. 11; British Iron and Steel Federation, nos. 44, 45; Bryant & May Ltd., and The Science Museum, nos. 2, 3, 4, 5; Camera Press, nos. 23, 24, 39, 48; Arthur Christiansen, nos. 37, 38; Fire Protection Association, nos. 17, 18, 19, 20, 22; G.E.C., no. 29; *The Guardian*, no. 26; High Altitude Observatory, Boulder, Colorado, nos. 8, 9; Iraq Petroleum Co., no. 10; A. R. King, Melbourne, no. 30; Frank W. Lane (K. Berger), no. 41; London Midland Region (BR), no. 40; Mansell Collection, no. 16; Norman Martin, no. 25; M. Nimmo, no. 31; Paul Popper, nos. 13, 15, 32, 36, 42, 43; Radio Times Hulton Picture Library, no. 21; Sacramento Peak observatory, AFCRL, nos. 6, 7; Suddentscher Verlag, no. 35; United Kingdom Atomic Energy Authority, nos. 46, 47; U.S. Air Force, nos. 33, 34.

Though the writing and the selection of illustrations has naturally been the author's responsibility he must pay tribute to the active and enthusiastic support he has received from Mr Frank Lane, who provided most of the photographs from which the final selection was made, and who was unfailingly helpful with material and suggestions, and undertook a final checking of the manuscript.

List of Illustrations

Foreword

Air and earth and water are always with us but fire has to be acquired or made. Fire fascinates, at all times, in all places; there is magic in a flaring match; leaping flames seem alive; for centuries we have said 'fire is a good servant but a bad master'. Wild fire destroys but, tamed, it has helped to build the world we know.

This non-technical survey of fire, past and present, and how it affects man, has had to be selective; a full study would be encyclopaedic, but there is a list of books at the end for further reading or for reference.

Many byways have had to be ignored. There is nothing on, for example, nature's hot water geysers; 'anting' birds which appear to bathe in fire; firearms; the phosphorescent fire-fly; Charles Lamb's chinaman roasting his pork; the destruction of weeds by fire—but we could fill another, and much longer, book. Many modern uses of fire in industry are covered by books on specific aspects, such as fire in the steel or rubber industries.

The illustrations are linked yet independent. Many matters mentioned in the text can be found in the pictures, but some of the subjects illustrated are not mentioned in the text.

CHAPTER I

The Conquest of Fire

Air is all around us; earth is beneath us, even when covered by water; water is everywhere, essential to life; but fire, friendly fire, fire to be feared, is the element conquered by man, without which we cannot imagine civilization.

Fire is one of the main differences between animals and man. Whoever saw a dog sitting by a fire it had made for itself? Man has made fire his servant but even the most intelligent animal cannot make a fire.

Men must have realized the value of fire hundreds of thousands of years ago but we have to use our imagination on how they first brought it under control. There are a number of possibilities and there must have been many early attempts, fraught with danger and doomed to failure, before fire became part of daily life.

Untamed fire in its natural or wild state can be found in the red-hot lava thrown out by volcanoes, or in 'escapes' of natural gas which have caught light, or in a burning forest set on fire by lightning. Meteorites, 'burnt up' in their passage through the atmosphere from outer space, can arrive on earth red-hot. The friction of two dead pieces of wood rubbing together in the wind can lead to their smouldering, and cause fire if other dead dry wood or grass is nearby. Spontaneous combustion is also a source of fire, as when a heap of damp hay bursts into flame because of the rise in temperature caused by fermentation.

To primitive men warmth was probably the first attraction, and a hesitant approach to the source of the heat, the glowing lava or the burning bush, could have given them the idea of trying to have such a comfort always handy. Coupled with this would be the realization that the wild animals were frightened of fire and it could therefore be a protection. Somehow men had to solve the problems of getting fire from the various sources, keeping it alight and keeping it under control.

We can't know the facts but it is a safe assumption that some daring man risked his life to get hold of a blazing branch, or to detach a piece of red-hot lava from the mass pouring down the side of the volcano. This would happen not once but many times, for keeping it alight would be a tremendous problem. There would follow a series of discoveries, all commonplace to us today: that dry wood blazed and damp wood smouldered; the necessity of having the fire on rock or bare earth to keep it from spreading; realizing the necessity for a supply of fuel to be ready, to keep the fire going.

Not until man had fire did he start to use caves, which were dark and could harbour dangerous animals. Fire gave light and a fire at the entrance of the cave gave protection against wild beasts.

At first there was no question of *making* a fire, it was enough if it could be kept alight. In the early years of this century there were still primitive tribes who could not make fire but who had developed the knack of keeping it permanently alight. Because of the labour involved in fire-lighting many tribes who knew how to make fire preferred to keep one permanently burning.

There must have been a tremendous gap in time between using fire and fire-making. By an odd chance a man would produce fire without realizing how it had happened, and years of haphazard hoping might well pass before another spark, another flame, a fire, came into being by a man's labours. We live in a world of matches and lighters but if we had neither and wanted a fire we should face a problem most of us could not solve. We have heard that it is possible to make fire by 'rubbing sticks together' but few of us could do this successfully.

Making fire by 'rubbing sticks' is not the only method passed down from prehistoric times, and there are doubts that it was necessarily the first method, but it was the most widespread, as shown by its world-wide use by primitive tribes who have survived into the twentieth century, and had many variations. Again, we have to guess how it was first discovered. It has been suggested that it might have been through seeing by accident two dried, dead branches rubbing together.

The commonest variety of this method, the fire-drill, was twirling a pointed stick between the palms of the hands, the point being pressed into a recess or hole in a board, the 'hearth' board, until a wisp of smoke appeared from wood-dust produced by the friction. Careful blowing could produce a glow from which small chips of wood or some dried grass could be set alight. Under ideal conditions this could produce a spark in ten seconds but twenty to thirty seconds would be more normal. There is a skill in keeping the twirling stick in the hole and most of us would have smarting palms long before we saw smoke.

An improvement was the twisting of a bow-string round the drill, the bow being pulled rapidly to and fro, making for speedier revolving of the drill. An alternative was a leather thong which was passed round the drill and pulled backwards and forwards, generally by a second man while the first man kept the drill pressed down into the recess by a 'cap', or hollowed piece of wood, on top. Without the second man the cap would be held in the mouth. Another, easier, way was to use a pliant stick which, bowed in the middle, enabled it to be 'cranked' against the hearth, in this case held vertically against a tree or rock.

The fire-drill may have originated from the discovery that a pointed stick made a hole, from that, trying to drill a hole in wood and thus producing fire by accident. It is difficult for us, in these days of rapid scientific progress, to appreciate the chance nature of primitive man's discoveries and that something which had happened by accident might not be repeated for a long time, perhaps years. A discovery might well be made in various parts of the world, not necessarily spreading from one source. Various timbers would have to be the subject of experiment before the best types for rapid fire production were discovered.

The fire-plough, rubbing a stick briskly up and down a grooved wooden hearth-board, was another method producing the same result, the wisp of smoke, the glow, the fire. This was favoured in the Pacific islands where a certain type of wood gave speedy results to the 'ploughing'.

Because of the sharp edge which can be obtained on split bamboo, a third method, the fire-saw, in which the sharp edge is sawn against the edge of the hearth-board (sometimes the board is drawn against the sharp piece of bamboo), is practised wherever bamboo is abundant.

It is possible that, before making fire with wood, man was fire-making by the accident of striking sparks when tool-making, hitting one type of stone on another to produce a sharp-pointed implement. The sparks, falling on dry vegetation, could cause a blaze. Such an accident might recur several times before it was realized that this could be accepted as a certain way of starting a fire.

This percussion method of fire-making became the standard way for many centuries in civilized countries. There might be refinements but the basis was the same. The pyrites and flints found in prehistoric barrows later became the piece of steel, flint and tinder (often a piece of charred cloth) carried in the tinder box. 'Striking' fire was often a nuisance, which is why most households kept at least one small fire going all the time, from which was lit anything needful, whether for lighting, cooking or even smoking.

Through the centuries both tinder boxes and the steels became most decorative and ornate and nowadays are eagerly collected. They became out-of-date and collector's items as recently as about 1830, with the invention of matches, and 'tinder and flint' became one of those terms giving flavour to historical novels.

After wood and stone comes air, with a third way of making fire. The fire-pump is certainly not primitive but its origins are unknown. It consisted of a piston in a cylinder, and heated air by compression through rapid pumping, the tinder being in a groove in the side of the cylinder. The fire-pump could be quite small, only two or three inches long, handy for carrying. From South-east Asia it spread to Malaya and the Philippines but is unknown elsewhere.

Before the lenses we know today in telescopes and microscopes and spectacles could be made we had to have glass, but there is a 'natural' glass, obsidian, a product of volcanic eruptions. Because of its hardness and the sharp edges obtainable when it is split, it was used by early man when weapon making, it produced deadly spear-heads, for example. In thin pieces obsidian can be translucent or transparent. From the chipping and flaking necessary to form weapons a crude lens could be accidentally produced, and if the rays of the sun fell on this at a certain angle the focusing of heat could cause a fire, as can our pocket magnifying glass. Again there would have been the long delay before men realized how and why the fire was produced but the method did ultimately come into use. It had the great disadvantage that it needed bright sunlight before it could be operative.

How man first got control of fire we shall never know but we can draw some conclusions from the fire-making and fire-keeping habits practised by tribes still existing in remote parts of the world, in the forests of Brazil, in the Great Australian desert, and in Tierra del Fuego (the Land of Fire), so-called by the earliest voyagers because of the fires seen ashore as their ships sailed by. Other evidence comes from archaeological discoveries and enables us to date, if only very roughly in terms of thousands of years, the early use of fire and the methods used.

When it comes to dates in the far-distant past a hundred thousand years is of no great importance. Close dating is impossible and though there is evidence of the use of fire about half-a-million years ago it might date from a hundred thousand years less, about 400,000 years ago, or it might be even more ancient as the species of man with whom this use of fire is associated can have ranged the earth up to a million years ago.

In the Acheulian period (from St Acheul in France, where some of the earliest remains associated with this particular culture were discovered—for example, hand-axes of a definite and finer shape than their predecessors), fire was in use. The Acheulian hunters about 300,000 to 250,000 years ago, left such traces in southern Africa and in Spain, but there are no traces of fire in Kenya, where they have also been identified. It is possible that in warmer climates they did not need fire.

One of the difficulties of assessing the early use of fire is the uncertainty of whether a fire was originated by man or was an accident of nature. There is the possibility that fires were started deliberately in grass lands to drive wild animals towards cliffs, but dry grass could be fired by lightning and result in trapped beasts hurling themselves over the cliffs to escape the flames. Scorched earth above and a mass of bones at the foot of a cliff can have more than one explanation. In some areas where ancient man has left his traces, reddened, burnt earth could well have arisen from volcanic action.

The present fragmentary evidence indicates that fire was first used in Central Asia, coming to Europe much later, and later still to Africa, and 'later' can mean a hundred thousand years in time for a matter of five thousand miles in space.

Whenever tribes have survived under primitive conditions into the nineteenth and twentieth centuries they have known how to make fire, with the exception of the people of the Andaman Islands, in the Bay of Bengal, who have fire but cannot make it. Either they have never mastered the art or have forgotten it at some time in the past. Some of the Congo pygmies do not make fire but as they are able to 'borrow' from neighbouring tribes when their fires go out it may be a case of laziness rather than ignorance. In South America there is a tribe who keep their fires going on a clay base in canoes, which would appear to be a precaution against fire getting out of control, but though not making fire themselves it is unlikely that they were completely ignorant of the technique. They did not suffer the comparative isolation of the Andaman islanders.

Once men had fire which meant warmth and protection, other uses were gradually discovered. Implements and weapons of wood could be hardened in the fire, making them stronger and more deadly. But the great discovery was the use of fire for cooking. Again we have to guess how it may have happened. A piece of meat brought into camp from a successful hunt and dropped into the fire by accident, or the discovery of a half-roasted carcass after a forest fire—whatever the origin, with it came the possibility of having meat more tender, tastier, more digestible. You can imagine the experiments which then started, never to cease, experiments which have gone on for tens of thousands of years and are still going on in our homes today. Cooking is now regarded as so essential to civilization that there is a never ending stream of books to meet an insatiable demand, helping to avoid what must have been the trial and error methods of the earliest cooks.

From straightforward cooking over the fire came later the discovery of cooking by boiling. The earliest heating of water would be by dropping hot stones into leather vessels containing the water. Kilns and coal-burning came into evidence in Central Europe about 50,000 years ago, associated with mammoth hunters. The kiln, or oven, was probably used for cooking and the coal-burning arose from coal measures at the surface in an area which had a shortage of the timber normally used by man for his fires. Pottery would come long after, again most probably one of those chance discoveries from some clay being discovered baked hard after being in contact with a fire. It is probable that one of the first adaptations of this discovery was coating wicker baskets with clay and thus making waterproof containers. This may well have been as long ago as 10,000 years B.C. although definite pottery remains in Britain are only four to five thousand years old.

Early pottery was heavy and clumsy and rarely carried about on long journeys or by hunting parties, so boiling was a luxury and was regarded by Indians of the North American plains, for example, as appropriate to, and synonymous with a feast. After the long period covering the discovery of fire-making and its various techniques, pottery and metal working by fire are comparatively modern, most evidences coming within a limit of 5,000 years ago for pottery and 3,000 years for metal-working.

The discovery and conquest of fire was now passing beyond the realms of pre-history, the archaeological research, the cautious deductions and inevitable assumptions in which inspired guesswork had to play its part.

The Fire Makers

'*They produce fire both by collision and by attrition; the former by striking two stones one against another, on one of which a good deal of brimstone is rubbed. The latter method is with two pieces of wood, one of which is a stick of about eighteen inches in length, and the other a flat piece. The pointed end of the stick they pressed upon the other, whirling it nimbly round as a drill, thus producing fire in a few minutes.*'

Captain Cook, 1778 (in the Bering Strait Area)

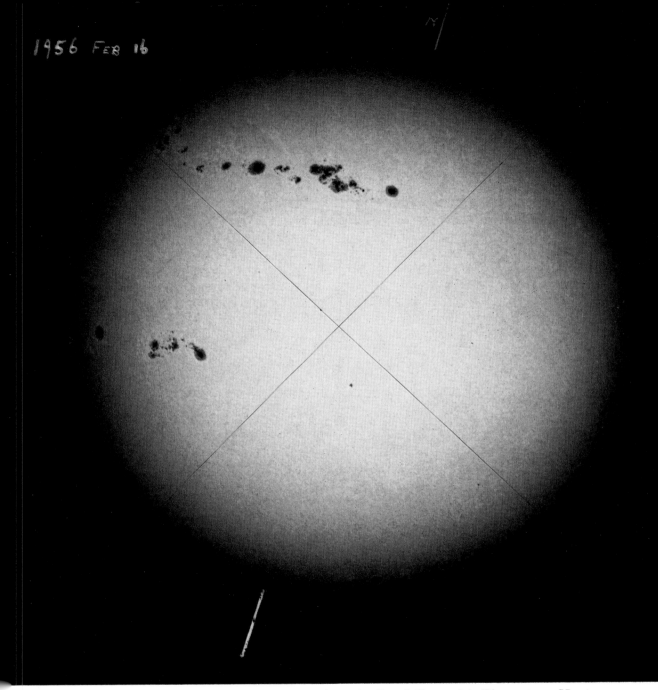

1. Photograph of the sun taken with a heliograph at the Royal Greenwich Observatory, Herstmonceux Castle, Sussex, on 16th February 1956. The extensive belt of sun-spots in the northern hemisphere comprises several separate sun-spot groups in approximately the same latitude. For scale—the diameter of the earth is less than 1/100th of the sun's diameter.

2. *Above:* A native of the Gran Chaco of Bolivia drilling fire. This photograph was taken during a Swedish expedition in South America in 1901-2.

3. *Below:* Two natives of the Nilgiri hills in India making fire with a Thong Fire-drill. This, and the two following photographs, were taken in the early years of this century.

4. *Above:* Two natives of Malabar in India making fire with a simple Fire-saw. Because of the sharp edges of split bamboo this sawing method is common where bamboo is abundant.

5. *Below:* Two New Zealand Maoris making fire with a Fire-plough. This brisk rubbing of a stick up and down a grooved board was favoured in the Pacific islands where a certain type of wood gave speedy results.

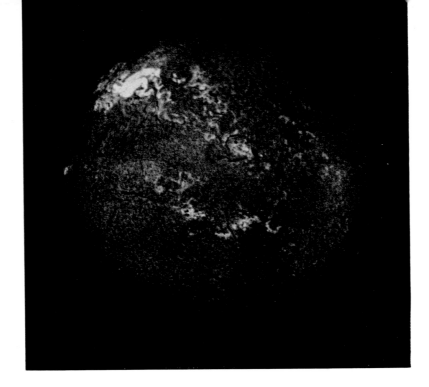

6. *Above:* The sun, taken by a special instrument that photographs only red light. The bright area in the north-west is a great flare, which may last a minute or an hour. The dark bands and streaks are flaming prominences, sheets of fiery hydrogen, which may be thousands of miles long and extend thousands of miles into space. Over a million earths could be contained within the sun, with room to spare.

7. *Below:* Close-up of sun-spots showing the tendency to link up in groups.

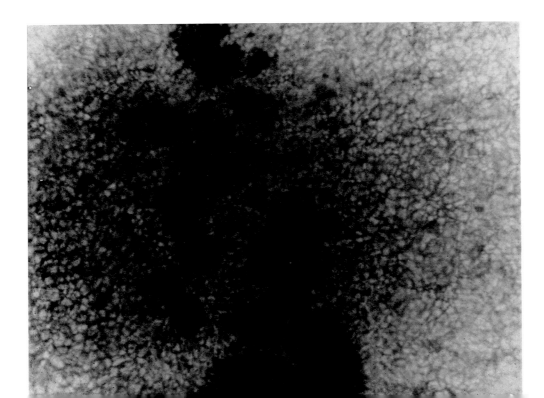

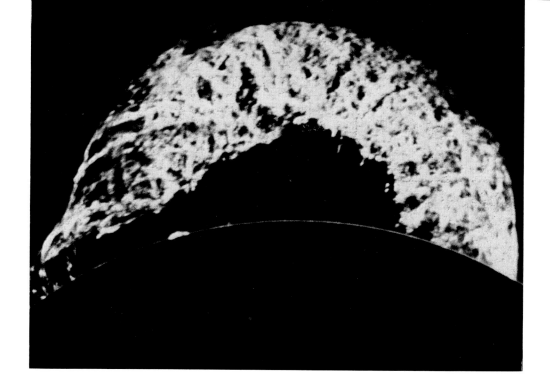

8. *Above:* Taken on 4th June 1946, the early stages of the largest eruption-type prominence seen up to then. Within an hour it became nearly as large as the sun only to disappear within a few hours.

9. *Below:* The solar corona during an eclipse, seen in Bolivia on 12th November, 1966.

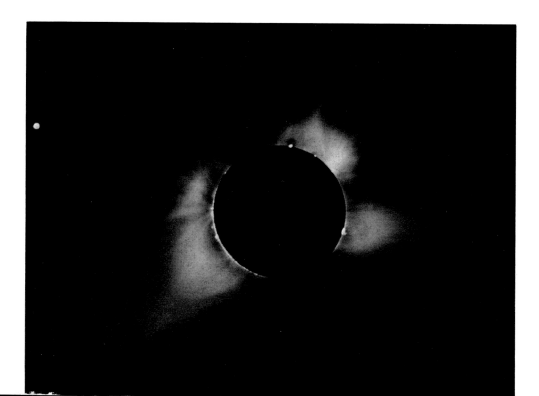

10. The sacred Eternal Fires at Baba Gurger, Kirkup, where oil, escaping from the earth, became ignited at some time in the past. These Eternal Fires have been worshipped for centuries.

11. From a pre-Inca Temple of the Sun at Tiahuanaco in South America. The centre figure is a Sun God, but it is not known what all the little running figures each side represent.

12. A solar-energy research laboratory in France, near the Eastern Pyrenees, seen in the background. A mirror, forty-three feet square, reflects the sun's rays into the facing parabolic mirror, which is composed of 3,500 separate small mirrors. In the centre is the solar oven in a metal tower. The concentrated sun-rays produce temperatures of over 2,500° Centigrade.

13. There is an ancient link in men's minds between volcanic eruptions and gods or spirits to be pro-pitiated. Dancers in Mexico are here seen trying to calm (or perhaps to frighten!) the spirits responsible for the eruption to be seen in the background.

14. *Above:* In 1937 a Gypsy Wedding was performed in public. As part of the ceremony the bride and groom had to jump through fire together.

15. *Below:* At Burghead in Scotland they still 'burn the Clavie' on New Year's day of the Old Calendar, now 12th January. A flaming tar-barrel is carried round the village before being burnt on a bonfire at a ruined Roman altar. Pieces of the burnt 'clavie' put up chimneys are supposed to keep witches away.

16. Old St. Paul's Cathedral being destroyed in the Great Fire of London of 1666. Picture taken from an old engraving.

View of the Stad House and the Engines for extinguishing Fire at — AMSTERDAM — Vüe de la Maison de Ville & les Pompes pour éteindre le Feu a — AMSTERDAM —

17. Fire-fighting practice in Amsterdam, probably in the late seventeenth century. It is thought to show the flexible hose invented by van der Heidens. The force of the jets of water is much exaggerated.

18. This manual fire engine at work in the mid-eighteenth century is illustrated in an advertisement put out by Elizabeth Nuttall of London and referred to on page 32.

19. A picture by William Heath showing the burning of the Houses of Parliament in 1834. Manually operated engines are shown, as in the previous two illustrations and though more efficient they could not cope, and of the buildings involved only Westminster Hall was saved.

20. This American 'steamer' (worked by steam and not manually), of 1872, looks too handsome, with its patterned wheels and complicated assemblage of lamps and wheels of varying sizes, for real-life use.

21. A vivid depiction of the destruction of ships of the Spanish Armada by English fire-ships. It must be regarded as highly imaginative in many details.

22. Galloping horses drawing a 'steamer' of the Metropolitan Fire Brigade through old Temple Bar in the Strand. Horse-drawn fire-engines could still be seen in London well into this century. The drawing comes from an 'Illustrated London News' of 1869.

23. Fire-walking is generally, but not always, part of a religious ceremony, possibly of purification, possibly to ensure good harvests. The practice is known throughout the world, from the Balkans to Japan. Here are Hindus in Singapore treading on burning coals at a ceremony held in October 1950.

CHAPTER 2

Sun:
The Greatest Fire We Know

Is there any other single object in our lives which so dominates them as does the glorious, warming, scorching sun? Every year many people in temperate zones pay out vast sums on holidays in search of the sun. As a source of light and heat, the ripener of crops, producer of a feeling of euphoria, of well-being, it is little wonder that the sun has been worshipped as a god, under a variety of names, for thousands of years, and that its disappearance, whether nightly or by temporary eclipse, could cause alarm and despondency.

There is the story of the two Chinese astronomers who, some four thousand years ago, failed to predict an eclipse. They were held responsible for the near loss of the sun and lost their heads to the Royal Executioner. The sun came back obligingly because of the vigorous counter-attack by flights of arrows, fired at the dragon who tried to eat the sun.

The full magnificence of the sun cannot be understood until it is hidden, eclipsed by the moon. Only then can the great solar flares and the flaming corona be seen to full advantage. Only a total eclipse enables us to see this crown of glory surrounding the sun. It is regarded as the most wonderful and impressive sight in the field of natural phenomena. Unfortunately total eclipses are not very frequent in any one part of the world. In the British Isles, for example, the next total eclipse to be seen will not be until August 1999, and the next after that not until 2135. The 1999 eclipse should be visible from near the Cornish coast, weather permitting.

The number of partial or total eclipses of the sun visible somewhere in the world in any one year can vary from two to five. These can often occur at comparatively inaccessible places, remembering that water covers nearly three-quarters of the earth's surface. Occasionally astronomers hire aircraft to 'chase the eclipse' which, in any case, normally lasts approximately only five to seven minutes. One advantage of an aircraft is that it can probably get above cloud cover when there is poor visibility on the ground, but it does not allow for the use of any heavy or large scientific instruments for observations.

The one total eclipse of the sun in 1967, visible over much of South Africa and Antarctica as partial, was total over only a thin strip of ocean, near the South Sandwich Islands. To take another example, the total eclipse of the sun in 1950 was visible from the North Pole and north-eastern Siberia, and in the most westerly of the Aleutian Islands, where the period of total eclipse was only about one-and-a-quarter minutes.

The sun's diameter is over a hundred times the diameter of the earth; in mass it could contain over a million earths, with room to spare; it is 93 million miles away, its light and heat taking just over eight minutes to reach the earth. The heart of the sun has a temperature estimated at fifteen to twenty million degrees Centigrade.

The sun is the great 'power-house' of our part of the universe, responsible for a continual production of energy on such a tremendous scale that it is difficult to convey it in figures. It has been likened to a beneficent super H-bomb, equal in power to *millions* of the destructive H-bombs we have succeeded in producing on earth. Producing this energy means a loss of mass to the sun of about four million tons every *second*, but the size of the sun means it can go on losing at this rate for millions of years with little difference to the amount of energy it pours out.

This energy is radiated in every direction and the earth gets its share but, bearing in mind its distance from the sun and comparative size in space, it is a minute proportion of the whole. It amounts to one part in two thousand million, 1/2,000,000,000th, and a high proportion of this is reflected back into space by earth's atmosphere. In spite of this the amount we receive from the sun is far more than the total energy we produce and use ourselves. The energy from the sun received by an acre of ground in a hot and comparatively cloudless climate, such as Egypt's for example, in one year, would equal the energy produced by burning over a thousand tons of coal.

Though we use little enough of the sun's energy by converting it into power, without this same energy we should not exist. It creates the weather, making water evaporate and the winds blow. Without it there would be no plant life, the basis of all life on earth.

The temperature on the surface of the sun is about 6,000° Centigrade (about 10,000° Fahrenheit). This surface is not like that of the earth but entirely gaseous and forever in a state of turbulent motion, with great flares and depressions continually forming and disappearing. It is called the photosphere—the light sphere. It is the sun we see when we can safely look at it when it is dimmed by cloud, mist, smoke or fog. To look straight into the full, undimmed sun is likely to cause permanent damage to the eyes, perhaps to the point of blindness.

Above the photosphere is the chromosphere—the colour sphere—and this, showing as a pink or rosy glow at a time of eclipse, can be regarded as the lower portion of the sun's atmosphere. Being less dense in consistency than the photosphere it is in a state of greater agitation and turmoil, throwing out great flaming streams of gas. Its depth is estimated at 30,000 miles, three times the distance between London, or New York, and Sydney in Australia, and more than the circumference of the earth.

Beyond the chromosphere is the corona, the outer atmosphere. In fact they naturally merge with one another as there cannot be a strict line of demarcation between them. The corona—the crown—is the brilliant halo round the sun which, because of the white-hot radiance of the photosphere, can only be seen at a total eclipse, and its breath-taking beauty makes viewing an eclipse a unique experience.

The corona flares out into space with a temperature far greater than that at the surface. The 6,000° Centigrade of the photosphere goes up to 1,000,000° (one million) in the corona. This is not what would be expected, the expectation being that away from the sun's surface the temperature should go down. Why it goes up instead of down is one of those many mysteries which make the sun such a fascinating study and men will be formulating theories and arguing about it for probably many thousands of years to come.

The inner corona extends for about 100,000 miles out, and beyond that, extending in ever diminishing density is the outer corona, to which it is impossible to put final boundaries—in fact it has been said that the earth probably comes within its bounds, though by then it is in a very attenuated, not to say invisible, form.

Among the phenomena of the sun which have their effect on the earth are the sun-spots which appear in the photosphere. These are forever forming and disappearing in a regular cycle which averages just over eleven years from peak to peak. First appearing between the sun's latitudes 30° to 40°, rarely if ever appearing above 45°, they gradually increase in number, meantime steadily moving from north and south towards the equator where they disappear, about which time the new sequence begins with the appearance of fresh spots, around the 35° latitudes. The individual spots last only a short time, it may be only a day or, under exceptional circumstances, for as long as two hundred days.

Because of the continual appearance of other spots the overall growth, move-ment and decline remains. The build up to the maximum activity generally takes three to four years and the decline to disappearance about seven to eight years.

This eleven-year cycle has an odd and unexpected effect on trees. It can be traced in the annual rings which enable us to calculate the length of life of a tree when it is felled.

'Spots' are not neglible blemishes on the face of the sun but large and actively whirling masses, probably due to the inherent instability in the heart of the sun. They are generally saucer-shaped depressions, but as they can be five or six hundred miles deep in the centre their magnitude is difficult to grasp. The largest observed sun-spot on which reliable data is available appeared in 1947 and covered seven million square miles, a space which could accommodate a hundred earths. Spots appear darker than the surrounding photosphere because of their lower temperature, about 4,000° against the photosphere's 6,000° Centigrade.

Associated with sun-spots are the great solar flares, blazing into an activity which may go in a few minutes or last for several hours. When in 1942 radar screens were jammed with radio signals it was thought at first that the Germans had stolen a march on us. A scientist discovered very quickly that the jamming came from the sun where there was a big sun-spot at the time and a great magnetic storm was raging. Further investigations revealed that the sun was sending out radio waves all the time and when sun-spot activity was at its maximum and great flares were leaping out, covering anything from a million to a thousand million square miles, magnetic storms were probable, putting both radio and radar out of action.

The Northern Lights, the Aurora Borealis, of northern latitudes, and the Aurora Australis of the south, are visible manifestations of what we can only describe at present as something in the nature of electrical discharges from the sun. These beautiful, many-coloured 'curtains', always more numerous at the peak of sun-spot activity, are rarely visible as far south as London or New York in the northern hemisphere, but in the north of Norway or Sweden, or in the Hudson Bay area, they are to be seen on average about a hundred times in a year, in varying degrees of intensity. As one gets nearer to the magnetic poles, on which their activity appears to be centred, they tend to disappear.

As well as the flares associated with sun-spots the sun has a number of pro-minences, sheets of flaming hydrogen, sometimes hundreds of thousands of miles long and shooting up to heights of anything from 15,000 to 150,000 miles, and in extreme cases going half-a-million miles out into space, but once again, they cannot normally be seen unless the sun's disc is dimmed by an eclipse. With the invention of the spectroheliograph in 1892, and the subsequent improvements made to it, astronomers were at last able to examine the corona, the flares, the prominences, without having to wait for an eclipse. The essential feature of the spectroheliograph is an extremely narrow slit, about one-tenth of a millimetre wide, less than one two-hundred-and-fiftieth part of an inch, through which the sun's light enters. It is then broken down by a series of prisms, reassembled by further prisms, and photographed, the whole sun being covered by a series of photographs governed by a slow clockwork movement incorporated in the instrument. Needless to say the result has none of the brilliance and beauty as seen by the naked eye at times of total eclipse.

Man may achieve a landing on the moon but the sun is beyond the bounds of all such physical exploration. It is our nearest true star, the next nearest star being 25 million, million miles away (25,000,000,000,000), and though that may make us feel closer to the sun we have so far only managed to send a satellite less than a third of the way. In May 1966 an unmanned spacecraft went within 76 million miles of the sun and over three years previously, in December 1962, the American Mariner II, 29 million miles on the way, was still 64 million miles from the sun. Up to the Spring of 1967, those two journeys are the closest we have sent probing spacecraft towards our nearest star. It is considered possible that specially designed craft could get within 10 million, perhaps to within 5 million miles of the sun, which would provide most valuable data for astronomers. Such a craft would have to be powered by a form of solar cell getting power from the sun but it would have to be a new type of cell.

The present solar cells lose power when they get too hot and would not operate beyond 30 to 40 million miles from the sun. There are a lot of experiments still to be made before we can successfully probe its near neighbourhood and solve the problems which at present are the subject of theories and inspired guesswork.

The power we receive from the sun is responsible for all the energy on earth but we use little by adaptation. The use of solar power through solar furnaces, solar batteries, solar heating, is in its infancy though capable of tremendous developments. Our debt to the sun lies in the fact that through sunlight plants grow, chlorophyll playing its part in converting this sunlight, and the energy which goes with it, into the chemical energy responsible for plant growth.

Behind the change from chemical substances into proteins and carbohydrates, the essential backgrounds to foods which keep us alive, lies the sun. Given air, earth and water sun is still needed to make plants grow—and all life depends on plant life. Animals—mammals, insects, fish, birds, man, all by direct or indirect eating of plants or their fruits, whether herbivores, carnivores or scavengers, depend on plant life, and plants depend on the sun.

The complicated part which chlorophyll plays (and it is far more than green colouring matter in plants) in the process called 'photosynthesis', is still subject to scientists' 'how and why' investigations. Chlorophyll aids in the nourishment of plants by absorbing carbon dioxide from the atmosphere and converting the raw material from the air and the soil, by this process of photosynthesis, into carbo-hydrates, into the living plant. How it happens we don't know but what is certain is that chlorophyll absorbs the radiant energy which comes from the sun and through that accomplishes the necessary chemical changes. This means that all living organisms derive their energy ultimately from the sun.

It is sometimes easier for us to think of energy in terms of the materials we use and the way we use them in modern life but whatever is used still shows our debt to the sun. We know that coal is the product of condensed and compressed plants which lived millions of years ago, now giving back through fire the energy absorbed from the sun all that time ago, but oil also is now regarded as the result of long slow accumulation of fragments of plant and animal life (most probably plankton, which is so prolific in the seas and oceans) the result of millions of years of change and compression. What is now called 'town gas' is derived from coal but we are now beginning to get supplies of 'natural gas' and this is the product of similar materials and conditions to those which produce oil. It is only to be expected that the two are often found close to one another, and sometimes mixed to a greater or lesser degree in oilfield or gasfield.

Coal, oil or gas are fuels for supplying energy to drive the turbines which produce electricity. The main source of power for this purpose, water-power, responsible for about half the world's electricity, also comes via the sun. The evaporation of water, the winds which carry the water inland to descend as rain and thus create the lakes and rivers which provide this water-power, have the sun as the primary cause, and so we are led back to it as the source of energy we use in the world we know, whether it comes from coal, gas, oil or electricity.

So little do we know of how and why all these aspects of the sun work to these ends, so little do we know of the basic facts that we are reminded of Sir Isaac

Newton's lament, 'I do not know what I may appear to the world, but to myself I seem to have been only a boy playing on the seashore, and diverting myself in now and then finding a smoother pebble or a prettier shell than ordinary, whilst the great ocean of truth lay all undiscovered before me'. We have discovered a little more since Newton's day but our essential sun remains a mystery.

The Sunne in the Equinoctiall and Arcticke

'*. . . seeing all heat and colde proceed from the Sunne, by the meanes either of the Angle which his beames do make with the Horizon, or els by the long or short continuance of the Suns presence above ground: so that if the Sunnes beames do beat perpendicularly at right Angles, then there is one cause of heat, and if the Sunne do also long continue above the Horizon, then the heat thereby is much increased by accesse of this other cause, & so groweth to a kinde of extremity. And these two causes, as I sayd before, do most concurre under the two Tropicks, and therefore there is the greatest heat of the world. And likewise, where both these causes are most absent, there is greatest want of heat, and increase of colde (seeing that colde is nothing but the privation and absence of heat) and if one cause be wanting, and the other present, the effect will grow indifferent. Therefore this is to be understood, that the neerer any region is to the Equinoctiall, the higher the Sunne doth rise over their heads at noone, and so maketh either right or neere right Angles, but the Sunne tarieth with them so much the shorter time, and causeth shorter dayes, with longer and colder nights, to restore the domage of the day past, by reason of the moisture consumed by vapour. . . .*

'*This benefit of the Sunnes long continuance & increase of the day, doth augment so much the more in colde regions as they are nerer the poles, and ceaseth not increasing untill it come directly under the point of the pole Arcticke, where the Sunne continueth above ground the space of sixe moneths or halfe a yere together, and so the day is halfe a yere long, that is the time of the Sunnes being in the North signes, from the first degree of Aries untill the last of Virgo, that is all the time from our 10 day of March untill the 14 of September.*'

From Richard Hakluyt's *The English Voyages:* (1589–99)

CHAPTER 3

Fire Legends and Fire Worship

The Yana Indians of the west coast of North America have a story of the early conquest of fire. A man wanting fire saw a mountain throwing out sparks. With some companions he stole fire from the mountain but on the return journey one of the men carrying the fire dropped it, and everything in the world went up in flames. This 'theft' of fire from a volcano and subsequent major conflagration when the fire got out of control is as near to the 'history' of primitive times of tens of thousands of years ago as we are likely to get.

Old legends of the origins of fire can often have a core of fact, overlaid with a wealth of imaginative detail, as is the case with many of the Greek stories of the gods. Greek mythology, though not the earliest, is probably richest in tales of gods and fire.

Perhaps the most famous is that of Prometheus, who stole fire from heaven for the use of man, for which he was condemned by Zeus, greatest of the gods of Olympus, to eternal punishment, from which he was released later by Heracles. Heracles, under his Roman style of Hercules, is supposed to have abolished human sacrifices and established the worship of fire among the Sabines of central Italy. There are many variations and embellishments to the Prometheus legend, as for example whether he stole fire from the lightning, from the sun, or from the forge of Hephaestus.

Hephaestus, god of fire, subsequently identified by the Romans as Vulcan, was the god of smiths and metal-workers, and the active volcano Stromboli was his workshop. Another story places his workshop in Etna, where he forged Jove's thunderbolts. It is thought that his worship started in the area of the Mount Olympus in Lycia, in Asia Minor, where natural gases, which can be ignited, still escape from the soil. The Prometheus legend links the capture of fire with lightning, with volcanoes, with ignited gases, and with the sun itself, all obvious sources of fire for primitive man.

The Greek god of the sun was Helios, who drove his fiery chariot across the sky each day, returning by night to his starting point, via an underground river, by a golden boat which had been fashioned by Hephaestus. Phaethon, sometimes used as an alternative name for Helios, is more often accepted as the son of

Helios who after worrying his father, was allowed to drive the chariot of the sun across the heavens. He proved too weak to control the horses who, plunging out of the sky, came so close to the earth that it scorched the ground, whereupon Zeus hurled a thunderbolt and killed Phaethon.

Helios later became identified with Apollo, whose statue as sun-god, known as the Colossus of Rhodes, was one of the ancient Seven Wonders of the World. It was so large that when at last it fell into ruin it took nearly a thousand camels to take away the brass of which it was made.

The sun-god passed by various names, thus leading to much confusion when we try to disentangle the myths, stories, legends which have come down to us. The Greek Helios, or Phaethon, or Apollo, also called Phoebus, was Sol to the Romans. The Egyptian sun-god was Ra, though there were a variety of names covering the many aspects of the sun. For example, Aten was the solar disc, Khepera was the rising sun and Atmu the setting sun. Baal, often referred to as the Syrian sun-god, was also a covering name for all Syrian gods.

There were two towns named Heliopolis, city of the sun. One of these, in Syria, was renamed Baalbec. Baal was worshipped there by the Syrians and the Greeks identified Baal with Helios. The other Heliopolis was in lower Egypt and was the centre of Egyptian sun worship. To this town came the fabulous Phoenix every five hundred years, to cremate itself on the flames of the ever-burning fire in the temple. From the ashes came a new, young, reinvigorated Phoenix who would not return until another five hundred years had passed. But again, there are many versions of this story.

The other creature associated with fire was the salamander, reputed to be able to live in fire and to extinguish it by nature of its own coldness. But the salamander is not immune from burning, suffering like any other living being.

Hephaestus, our metal-working god with his subterranean activities, was sometimes regarded as the god of destructive fire, naturally enough in view of his close connection with volcanoes. In contrast was Vesta, goddess of the kindly hearth fire. From her came the name of the Vestal virgins, who had to tend the everburning fires in the temples. These fires were obviously inherited from the days when fire was dangerous to acquire and difficult to make; those primitive days when the men had to leave the fire to the care of the women, to be kept alight while they were away hunting.

Today we have the Undying Flame at the tomb of the Unknown Soldier at the Arc de Triomphe in Paris, a link with the temples of Greece and the fires of prehistoric times. Sacred eternal fires occur in many parts of the world. They are sometimes provided by nature as when ignited petroleum gas, escaping from the ground, gives the venerated 'Eternal Fires' of Kirkup in the Near East. Man-made fires are, or have been, the subject of wide-spread rituals. They are often the centre of annual ceremonies when the old fire is put out and a new one created. This was often associated with Fire Festivals held at Easter, or on May Day Eve, Walpurgis, one of the nights when the witches rode, or on May Day, when all fires and lights had to be extinguished before the new fire was kindled. The re-kindling often had to be done by the ancient method of rubbing two pieces of wood together, no flint, iron or steel being allowed. This annual extinguishing of old lights and creating a new light from which all others had to be lit is still practised in some churches.

The Beltane (or Beltaine) Fires, held regularly in Scotland up to two centuries ago, often included these observances, together with the practice of driving cattle through the fires, or between two fires, which was an accepted protection against witchcraft. This latter observance links with a custom of the Tartars who made strangers and visitors walk between two fires and who insisted that any gifts be carried between the fires, to destroy any 'magic' the visitors might have brought with them.

Fire is often regarded as a purifier, as when we speak of gold having been passed through the fire and thereby being purged of all dross. Passing through fire was often one of the important rites of initiation when the boys of a tribe were put through various ordeals after which they were accepted as men. The Nordic legend of the ring of fire through which the hero had to go to release the maiden, and which Wagner uses in his 'Ring' cycle of operas, may well have originated in memories of an initiation ceremony.

Reverting to tribal legends explaining the origin of fire, there is a picturesque story from North America where one Red Indian tribe said that buffaloes galloping over the prairies created fire. Again there is the possibility of truth behind the story. Amidst the thunder of hooves, stones being kicked this way and that beneath the feet of the charging animals, sparks could have been struck and these could have led to fire under drought conditions.

In an island off Australia fire was attributed to two aborigines accidentally rubbing sticks together. When sparks came and fire burst out they ran to the chief who, realizing the value of the fire, gave a torch he lit from it to one of the women with the instruction that she must guard it and keep it alight always. This is so close to the probable truth it can hardly be regarded as a myth.

A Phoenician story of the creation of man tells of the Wind and his wife having as children Life and Firstborn, who had children in their turn, who were the first to worship the sun. Their descendants were Light, Fire and Flame, who discovered the use of fire; which sounds confusing. Owing to the difficulties of deciphering the language of the Etruscans, who appeared in central Italy about 3,000 years ago, little is known of them, but Tina was their fire god and it has been claimed that the name persists in 'tinder', and in 'teine', the Celtic word for fire, this occurring in 'Beltaine', the name of the Fire Festivals referred to earlier.

Myths and legends grow into rites and observances. The stories bring in their train unexpected developments. To early man the sun was not merely the father of fire but also the giver of life. When midsummer came and he began his descent, days becoming shorter, he had to be aided, so fires were lit and incantations uttered to help him on his weary way. Of all the various times of the year which saw the bonfires lit Midsummer had the greatest and most numerous fires in the hope and expectation that they would help the sun when he was weakening.

Again, the sun could be captured, he might disappear one day and fail to return one morning, or the eclipse might mean total capture one day, so plans were made to catch him. In Peru nets were stretched between hills, the Eskimoes in the Arctic tried with meshes of string, the Australian aborigines also had their ideas of delaying the disappearance of the sun. The magic assumed terrifying forms as when human beings were sacrificed by Aztec priests in Mexico to give strength to the sun. In the Americas the sun assumed a central part of religious observances but because of the wiping out of records when the Spaniards conquered the New World we know little of the origins and background of the civilizations they found there.

The holy fires burning forever in the temples of Greece had their parallels in Peru. The Incas had their temple fires tended by their virgins of the sun, re-kindled at a certain feast-time by reflection of the sun's rays from a mirror. Here also was human sacrifice to help the sun. The Inca kings were worshipped as sons of the sun and they regarded death as a call from their father to go and rest with him. The Inca empire extended far beyond the boundaries of modern Peru.

How much the Incas inherited, how much they developed from the race and religion which preceded them we do not know, but at Tiahuanaco is a pre-Inca temple to the sun with the largest gateway of its kind in the world.

The sacrifices and the ceremonies associated with the worship of the gods of fire and thunder, and with the sun, lasted for many centuries, gradually changing their nature with time. The pagan festival on the eve of November the 1st when the fires were lit to keep witches away became the All Saints' Day of the Christian churches, but old memories die hard and the Guy Fawkes episode in England possibly gave an excuse again for fires at that same time of the year though shifted to November the fifth.

Outside the various festivals came the fires lit at time of distress, the needfires, always made by wood-friction and regarded as a help, if not a cure, to get rid of plagues and diseases, whether suffered by beast or man. This was resorted to as late as 1785 in parts of Scotland to cure cattle of the infectious murrain.

A survival from old times about which there is much speculation is 'fire-walking', where people walk unscathed over beds of fire which spectators cannot approach because of the scorching heat. In Greece in recent years, on May the 22nd, St. Constantine's day, fire walkers crossed burning coal which had a temperature of about 180° Centigrade. In the Malaccas there is an annual festival where, after days of prayer and meditation, the participants work themselves into a frenzy before crossing white-hot charcoal fires. In islands in the South Seas stones are heated on which the firewalkers step. They claim there is no religious significance in their ceremony, which arises from a legend that members of the tribe were given immunity from being burned, by a god caught by a member of the tribe.

In September 1966 the magician Stromboli walked through glowing charcoal at a magicians' meeting at Hastings. He said it was based on the purification ceremony performed by Shinto priests in Japan. For the present it is another fire mystery.

Stonehenge, in the heart of southern Britain, was erected some 3,500 years ago. Although the arrangement of the stones was such that the alignment focused on a stone which marked the point at which the sun first appeared over the horizon on midsummer's day there is no evidence that it was in any way connected with the worship of the sun.

Fire-worship was at the heart of the Zoroastrian rituals. Zoroastrianism was one of the great religions of the world, founded by Zoroaster about 2,800 years ago. Fire was regarded as the source of life. When Persia was conquered by the Arabs in the seventh century the followers of Zoroaster fled to India. There they are known as Parsees and because of their standards of education, progressive outlook and practise of the good life, as enjoined by their religion, exercise an influence out of all proportion to their numbers. They can be regarded as the last of the fire-worshippers among the educated people in the world. They explain their worship of fire as being symbolic and not of fire itself.

Certainly both as a symbol and for itself, fire, whether in its earthly manifestations or its dominant role as the sun in heaven, has evoked wonder and worship from man for many thousands of years.

Sorcery in the North-west Passage

'*Their custome is as often as they go from us, still at their returne to make a new truce, in this sort, holding his hand up to the Sun with a lowd voice he crieth Ylyaoute, and striketh his brest with like signes, being promised safety, he giveth credit. . . .*

'*They are witches, and have many kinds of inchantments, which they often used, but to small purpose, thankes be to God.*

'*Being among them at shore the fourth of July, one of them making a long oration, beganne to kindle a fire in this manner: he tooke a piece of a board wherein was a hole halfe thorow: into that hole he puts the end of a round stick like unto a bedstaffe, wetting the end thereof in Trane(oyle), and in fashion of a turner with a piece of lether, by his violent motion doeth very speedily produce fire: which done, with turfes he made a fire, into which with many words and strange gestures, he put diverse things, which wee supposed to be a sacrifice: my selfe and divers of my company standing by, they were desirous to have me go into the smoke, I willed them likewise to stand in the smoke, which they by no meanes would do. I then tooke one of them, and thrust him into the smoke, and willed one of my company to tread out the fire, & to spurne it into the sea, which was done to shew them that we did contemne their sorcery.*'

From Richard Hakluyt's *The English Voyages:*
The Second Voyage of Mr John Davis; 1586

CHAPTER 4

Fire the Destroyer

In spite of the wonder of its discovery, the grandeur and the worship, fire can be an evil and dangerous thing at its worst and it merits caution and respect at all times. Man has used it to destroy but accidents also happen with disastrous results. Nature destroys by combustion, sometimes directly but often by the effects of volcanic action, lightning or meteorites, though nature often gives advance warnings.

Because of the material of which they are made books fall easy victims. When in ancient times that wise woman, the Sibyl, brought her nine Sibylline books to the king and he would not pay her price she burnt three and offered the six at the same price. As he still refused to buy she burnt another three and offered the last three at the price she had asked for the nine. Impressed, the king bought the three. We shall never know whether they were worth the money for they were destroyed when the Temple of Jupiter, where they were kept, was burnt down in 83 B.C. The Sibyl was not available to rewrite them but when a manuscript of one of the volumes of Carlyle's FRENCH REVOLUTION was destroyed, by a maid putting it on the fire, he was able to rewrite it so here fire did not conquer.

The library at Alexandria, founded about 290 B.C., was in its time the great repository of learning, with about half-a-million books, or 'rolls', as they were in those days. A quantity were destroyed in the course of Caesar's siege in 47 B.C. but the whole library was destroyed by the Arabs seven hundred years later because they said all necessary knowledge was contained in the Koran. The story goes that the burning of the books heated the city baths for six months, but that they were not entirely wasted is poor consolation—if the story is true.

This was not the last time that men used fire in an attempt to destroy ideas. Heretics were burnt at the stake in the Middle Ages and the Nazis had a bonfire of books they thought pernicious in the nineteen-thirties.

The burning of towns in times of war was so commonplace in the Middle Ages that, in Central Europe, those that never suffered such a fate were in a minority. Unfortunately such destruction has not been limited to past ages, and in the last war many cities suffered cruelly by fire as a result of bombing—London, Coventry, Dresden and Hiroshima spring to mind. In modern war flamethrowers and napalm bombs replace the Greek Fire of thirteen hundred years ago. Greek Fire was made of sulphur, naphtha, and either quicklime or nitre. Made into a ball and ejected from a tube by an air or water pump, with a possible range of fifty yards, it was claimed to be unquenchable. First used at Constantinople by the Greeks it was responsible for the almost total annihilation of a Saracen fleet in A.D. 718.

A few centuries later and fire again played a decisive part in a sea-battle when Drake sent his 'fire-ships' careering into the great Spanish Armada.

Nero, it is said, fiddled while Rome burned but it is of doubtful truth, as is also the statement that he set fire to the city. This great fire in A.D. 64 destroyed over half Rome and raged for more than six days. One definite fact in Nero's favour is that he afterwards rebuilt Rome to an improved plan with wider streets.

The most famous fire in English history was an accident, at least no evidence acceptable in a court of law has ever been produced to prove it otherwise. When the Great Fire of London took place in 1666 the magnitude of the disaster was not realized at first, and both the Lord Mayor and Mr Samuel Pepys went to bed after seeing it, soon after it began. The fire burnt for four days and consumed nearly the whole of the City within the Walls and much outside. It did lead to regulations designed to prevent any such tragedy in the future. Certainly no subsequent fire spread so fast and so far.

Another case where too much familiarity led to under-estimating the dangers and to even greater destruction was the earthquake which caused the great fire in Yokohama and Tokyo in 1923. With the collapse of houses, due to the earthquake, fires started and people made their way to open spaces where they could expect to be safe. In one place, where 40,000 people had taken refuge, a great fire tornado swept across and only a few hundreds survived. The dead were not burnt but died from carbon monoxide poisoning due to the oxygen being sucked out of the atmosphere by the flames. The total death roll by fire and earthquake in Tokyo was over 100,000. Fire was responsible for more damage than the earthquake. In Yokohama 60,000 buildings were burnt to the ground against 20,000 destroyed by the earthquake.

Man can equal nature in destruction. During the last war Tokyo burned again after bombing raids, with a loss of more than 100,000 lives.

Major accidental fires have occurred within the last hundred years, as when half Chicago was destroyed by fire within twenty-four hours in 1871. Modern fire-fighting techniques make it unlikely that any large city will ever again suffer such a major catastrophe from fire in peace-time.

One other major city fire should be mentioned here because it may well have changed the course of history. When the French reached Moscow in 1812 there is little doubt that the city was deliberately fired by the Russians to deprive the French of the possibility of using it for winter quarters. 'The Retreat from Moscow' has passed into the language as synonymous with defeat at the moment of victory.

One last reference to fire in history and that is to the non-fire celebrated to this day in Britain as Guy Fawkes day on November the Fifth. When the Chinese invented fireworks in the sixth century they would have been astonished to learn that their main use in Britain fourteen centuries later would be to celebrate a failure to blow up Parliament in the seventeenth century.

Just over two hundred years later, in 1834, a fire started which destroyed the whole of the Parliament buildings with the exception of Westminster Hall. It was one of those fires which the manual-operated engines of that day could not control, let alone conquer.

To most of us the cry of 'Fire!' often means a fire engine dashing by on its way to a burning building. A hundred years ago the engine drawn by galloping horses looked far more exciting than the fast efficient engines of today. Although the horses gave an impression of speed they were also a challenge to small boys who would 'race' them to the fire.

The first mention of any organization for fighting fires was in China, some six thousand years ago. Two thousand years ago the Romans had trained brigades of fire-fighters, though they failed to control the famous fire of Rome in Nero's time. Eight hundred years ago laws were introduced in England to control the use of too much inflammable material in buildings. The dangers of fire were realized from the very early days in towns and cities. The will to fight fire was there but the means were inadequate.

An advertisement put out about two hundred years ago by Elizabeth, widow of Adam Nuttall, Engine Maker to His Majesty's Royal Navy, states she 'Continues to make and sell Engines of all sorts for extinguishing of Fires, and watering Gardens, which play with a constant stream and prodigious force a large bore of water closely collected together, and thereby sooner extinguish the flames in Buildings, than any Engines hitherto contrived.' She delivers an emphatic attack in her Advertisement at Engines 'that have racks and chains' which 'become useless in a short time, and liable so to be when most wanted'. Elizabeth's manual engines needed from 8 to 22 men to operate them. The manually operated engine was still in use in the early years of this century.

24. The men, the ladders, the fire-engines, all are dwarfed by the mighty cloud of smoke at this rubber-factory fire at Watford, England. An added contrast is the peaceful suburban background to the threatening cloud.

26. Fighting a warehouse fire in Manchester, July 1966.

This one ↓

25. A grain warehouse on fire, at Newark, England, in February 1964. 2,500 tons of barley were destroyed and the overall loss was over £150,000. A wonderful picture of a furious fire.

27. When bush-fires swept Tasmania in February 1967 they destroyed several townships and invaded the outskirts of the capital, Hobart. There are chimney-stacks left standing when the wooden houses were burnt. Over fifty people lost their lives and thousands were rendered homeless.

28. *Above:* The smoking remains of this plastics factory in Bolton, England, in April, 1966, clearly shows the aftermath of a destructive fire.

29. *Below:* This destruction is through lightning. This house was struck in 1936 and is in White Plains, New York.

30. *Above:* A fire-tornado formed in a fire in the country, due to the turbulence in the atmosphere caused by the heat.

31. *Below:* A wild, raging fire on a Hampshire common with flames leaping up thirty feet or more.

32. *Above:* Boqueron volcano on San Benedicto island, 350 miles off the Pacific coast of Mexico, in September, 1952, showing the cone of the volcano, with lava flowing down to the sea.

33. *Below:* Lightning over erupting Vesuvius in March 1944. The red-hot lava shows up clearly in the night as it flows down the slopes of the volcano.

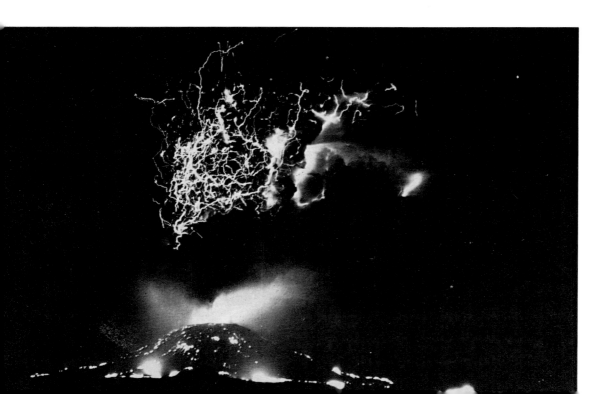

34. This volcano came up out of the Atlantic. The great cloud of smoke and steam rose a mile high, dwarfing the 115 feet high Capelinhos lighthouse on the isle of Faial in the Azores in October, 1957.

35. Kilauea volcano in Hawaii spouting molten lava and giving the appearance of a gigantic firework display.

36. Fireworks in Tokyo at the Midsummer Carnival, one occasion when fire is indicative of rejoicing and not danger.

37. *Above:* Lava rocks in Lake Myvatn, Iceland, help to create a scene of beauty with their fantastic shapes. The last eruption in this area took place about 250 years ago.

38. *Below:* This hot-spring in central Iceland is evidence of the trapped heat beneath the ground. It is remarkable how reliable and consistent, how dependable in timing, are so many of the hot-springs and geysers.

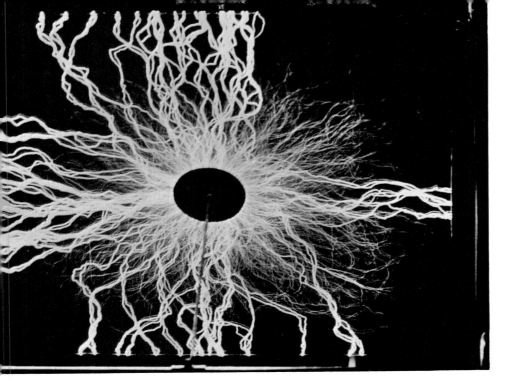

39. *Above:* Lightning in the laboratory is produced, complete with thunder effects, under high tension for research purposes.

40. With the increasing number of diesel and electric trains this steam engine is a rapidly vanishing sight—and there are less smuts and fewer embankment fires. 4-6-2 Locomotive no. 46227 on Shap Fell, 11th April, 1956.

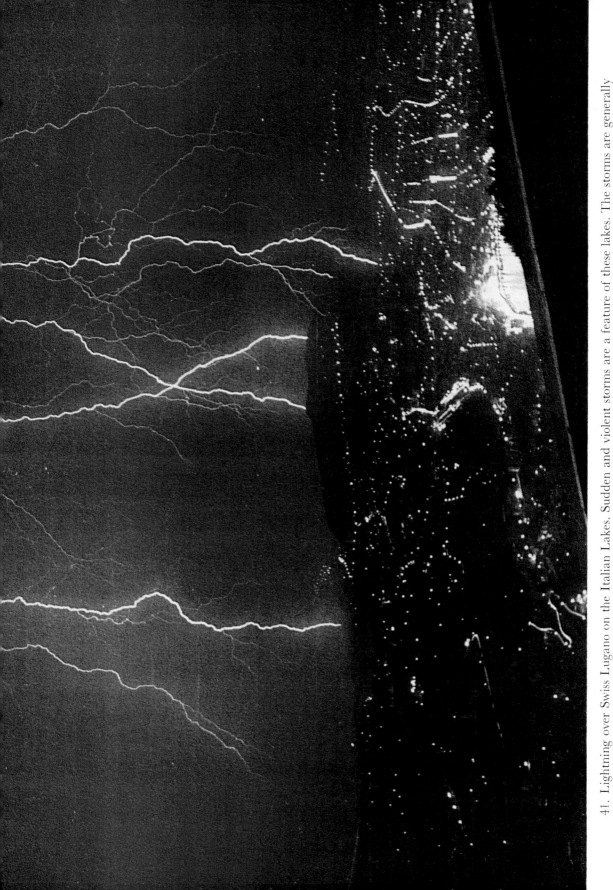

41. Lightning over Swiss Lugano on the Italian Lakes. Sudden and violent storms are a feature of these lakes. The storms are generally brief and often picturesque.

43. Gas-flare by day in the North Sea. Testing natural gas dis-covered in the North Sea drillings in December 1966.

42. Oil-flare by night in the jungle, at the Seria oilfield, Brunei.

45. Slagging off from Blast Furnace with protective clothing worn against the heat.

44. There is the glow of heat in this picture—charging molten iron into an L D Converter at the Ravenscraig Works of Colvilles Ltd.

47. This is the interior view of the great dome structure at Windscale shown in the previous illustration.

46. Atomic power in peace is responsible for the highly complicated Advanced Gas-cooled Reactor at Windscale.

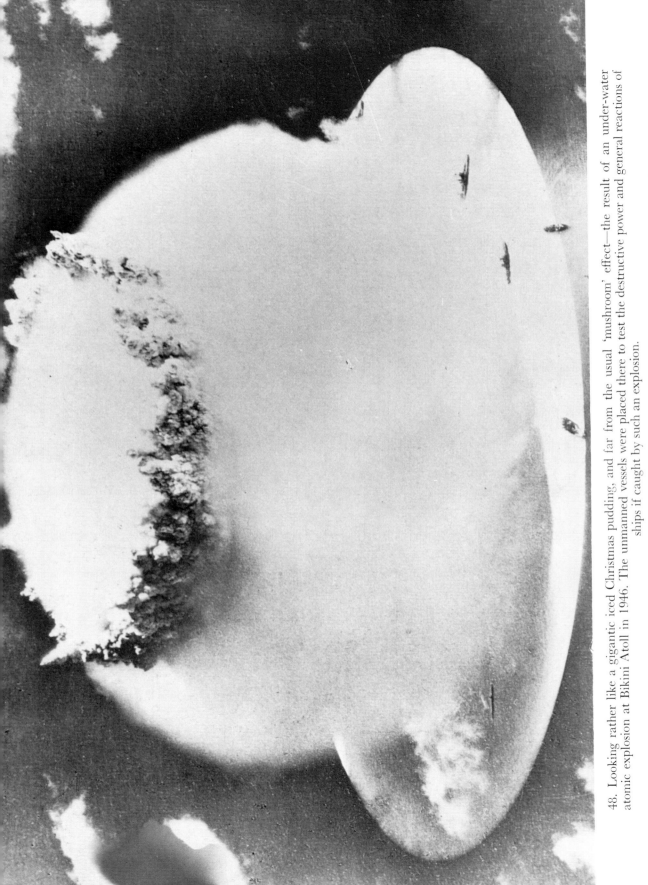

48. Looking rather like a gigantic iced Christmas pudding, and far from the usual 'mushroom' effect—the result of an under-water atomic explosion at Bikini Atoll in 1946. The unmanned vessels were placed there to test the destructive power and general reactions of ships if caught by such an explosion.

Forest fires happen every year but it is rare for them to invade towns as happened when bush fires in Tasmania, in February 1967, raged up to the outskirts of Hobart and destroyed 630 homes and 50 factories.

In myths handed down by the Hindu people is one of a great volcanic eruption in the sea. Brahma assigned it to the ocean as he knew it would have destroyed the land with its fiery blasts. Volcanoes are 'natural phenomena' with tremendous powers of destruction yet men go on living near many of them because of the rich soil, which means abundant harvests.

Beneath the crust of the earth are rocks so hot they are in a molten condition. In some places this molten rock bursts through the earth's surface with such force that it can spread death and destruction for miles around. As more and more forces its way out a hill is often formed which becomes a mountain as the years pass. This is not invariably the case, especially with underwater volcanic action which can produce volcanoes which disappear and reappear at sea level. A ship searching for one such volcano innocently halted just above the crater as it started to erupt. The ship disappeared completely, only wreckage being recovered.

One trouble about volcanoes is that they can go to sleep for hundreds of years, be deemed extinct, then suddenly come alive and start ejecting molten rock and red-hot lava. Tristan da Cunha came alive in 1961 but evidence suggests that it had not been active for about 3,500 years. In this case the population was safely evacuated, though some of them later returned, preferring to face the perils of volcanic action rather than the perils of Western civilization.

Two thousand years ago there was a flourishing countryside and settled towns around the extinct volcano Vesuvius, near Naples. A few earthquakes occurred but people didn't worry. One day in August in A.D. 79 Vesuvius erupted—and one thousand seven hundred years later people started to discover, by accident of digging, the towns of Pompeii and Herculaneum, buried and forgotten for centuries. The disaster was so sudden that in one place the preserved body of a Roman soldier was discovered, still 'on guard'.

That one product of volcanic action is extremely rich soil is emphasized when it is realized that the volcanic island of Java is one of the most densely populated areas in the world. It is thought that a great volcanic disaster was the reason why Java disappeared from history from around A.D. 1000 for several hundreds of years. That such an event was possible is borne out by the Krakatoa explosion of August 1883. The island of Krakatoa lies to the west of Java in the Sunda Straits. It was about 18 square miles in area. After the great eruption eleven square

c

miles of the island had disappeared. Few died from the explosion or the rain of burning ash but the tremendous tidal wave from this catastrophic outburst caused the deaths of over 36,000 people living on the shores of the Sundra Straits.

The warnings before volcanic action are rarely heeded. People do not want to panic needlessly and think and hope that the earth tremors and volcanic rumblings may subside. Krakatoa gave over three months' warning, and there was a warning of some weeks of another disaster, when a volcanic explosion blew out the side of Mount Pelee in the West Indies, half-way round the world from Krakatoa.

The town of St Pierre was five miles from Mount Pelee and the inhabitants thought they had nothing to fear in spite of the noises showing the volcano's activity. One citizen fled with his family to a nearby mountain, looked back, saw the side of Mount Pelee open and a blast of hot air and molten rock rush out straight at St Pierre. It took about 3 minutes for this death-dealing mixture to reach the town, and about 3 seconds to blanket it. When this erupted mass hit St Pierre it wiped the town out. 30,000 people died; rescuers found a man alive in the jail when they went in later. Death came quickly, by asphyxiation from the fumes and scorching from the heat, rather than by fire, but the fire raged in the town for several days.

Today we have become more cautious and when the Kilauea volcano in Hawaii became active in 1959, culminating in one of the worst eruptions the island has known in January 1960, which continued for a month, nobody was killed or injured.

Another potential destroyer with great speed and heat is lightning, which has been likened to the recharge of the earth from the sky, of the electricity which leaks from the earth on a cloudless day. Although it has been estimated that the earth is struck by lightning a hundred times a *second* we cannot regard it as a major hazard. The lightning conductors fitted to many buildings, and on ships, which conduct the electric charge safely to 'earth', have meant many less fires in towns and on the seas but it still has its dangers. In May 1967, after severe storms in many parts of England, newspapers carried reports of a man killed while cycling, a large house being destroyed by fire, a ton of masonry being dislodged from a church roof, and a small fire starting on an oil tanker, all as a result of being struck by lightning. It is impossible to guard against forest fires being started by such an event.

In yet another way nature takes a hand in causing destruction by heat. When foreign objects from outer space enter our atmosphere the friction caused by their tremendous speeds raises their temperature until they often glow with heat, and as the flash goes through the air we see a 'shooting star'. If the intruder is small it may never reach the earth but be burnt up on the way, but larger objects, which can weigh thousands of tons, can cause widespread devastation where they land, as did the one which landed in Siberia in 1908, the site of which was only traced twenty years later. For many miles around vegetation and animal life was completely wiped out. The weight has been variously estimated at anything between 2,000 and 40,000 tons.

These foreign bodies from outer space are the meteorites, the 'thunderbolts', the 'Stones from Heaven', and sources of many myths. Today they may well be responsible for some of the Unidentified Flying Objects which alarm many people.

In *Bleak House* Mr Krook, the rag and bone merchant, disappeared by spontaneous combustion and there are occasional reports of individuals who have disappeared, leaving behind only a heap of ashes and a bad smell, but such combustion of human beings can be regarded as of very doubtful validity. However, spontaneous combustion can occur in nature. Fermentation in a heap of hay can cause a rise in temperature until it bursts into flame, and there is a well authenticated report of a Dorset cliff where a 'pseudovolcanic eruption began in September 1826 and during a period of many months emitted considerable volumes of flame', which was attributed to the decomposition of iron pyrites in the shale, which was so rich in bitumen it was burnt as fuel in cottages nearby. Spontaneous combustion can be regarded as a minor interesting manifestation of fire in nature rather than a major risk.

We may never expect to control the lightning, the volcano or the meteorite but we can do much to control, if not completely conquer, the dangers of fire in civilized society.

CHAPTER 5

Fire, the Good Servant

The conquest of fire meant an increase in comfort; it lead to the prolongation of life; it made possible the achievements on which our civilization depends. When man started using fire for warming, for cooking and for metal-working he started on a road of discoveries to which there can be no end.

For the individual it was a great advance when he was able to carry with him his own fire-maker. The tinder and flint which was an essential part of one's personal possessions assumed great importance over the centuries, as is borne out by the elaborately carved and decorated fire-steels, tinder-pistols and tinder boxes men carried about. The invention of matches a hundred-and-forty years ago put an end to these, and was another great step forward—is there any lover of the 'good old days' still insisting on using tinder and flint? The largest manufacturer of matches in Great Britain produces forty-five thousand million matches every year. What is astonishing is that only one-fifth are safety matches, four-fifths being the 'strike anywhere' type.

The names of some early matches were often based on those of gods and goddesses associated with fire, as for example 'Vulcan' and 'Vestas', the latter a well-known match-name today.

Upon this simple ability to 'strike a light' is raised a vast edifice of fire, heating and lighting, which is so commonplace we rarely stop to think about it.

The first fuel was wood, and wood remained the chief fuel for tens of thousands of years. There might be a local use of coal where a seam chanced to surface, as happened in Central Europe 50,000 years ago, and there may have been oil fires—there is a story of Volga boatmen setting fire to oil-impregnated earth to warm themselves. It is assumed they took some precautions against the fire spreading.

When men were few and forests covered the lands trees could be felled and fires refuelled with no worry about a shortage, but as certain areas became densely populated demand outstripped supply and the forests disappeared. This happened in many parts of China and getting fuel became, after food, a main preoccupation of the peasants.

In Western Europe and America there are many alternatives but without the coal, gas, oil and electricity there could not have been the great technological advances of the last century.

Before the Romans came to Britain coal was being used and it is probable that the Romans learnt about coal from the Britons. Certainly there were stores of coal kept in various places along Hadrian's Wall. Coal would first have been discovered where it came to the surface near a cliff or on a beach and digging out the coal would ultimately mean digging into the ground, and that meant the start of coal-mining. Two-hundred-and-seventy years ago it was estimated that about three million tons of coal were burnt in Britain in a year and that the timber used in fires was the equivalent of half-a-million tons of coal. Today we mine about one hundred and eighty million tons of coal in Britain annually.

The burning of coal was, for centuries, wasteful because, being cheap, it was not burnt to get the maximum heat from the fire and it was not realized that more than warmth could be got from the burning coal. Only in comparatively modern times have the derivatives from coal, such as gas and coke, been developed. In Britain only 15 per cent of the coal produced goes into heating our homes. The main uses are for producing electricity, coke, gas, and industrial uses, such as in the making of steel.

Wood, as charcoal, was first used for smelting iron, and coal, as coke, enabled the iron and steel works to develop at a time when wood was no longer so plentiful and restrictions were being placed on its use. Today electricity is being increasingly used in steel works to produce the high temperatures needed.

Not only in heating our homes but in many industrial uses the four main sources of heat are sometimes in competition, sometimes complementary to one another. Coal is used to produce gas and electricity; electricity is used for mining the coal; oil and 'natural' gas are often found mixed or in adjacent 'fields'—the underground sources are known as oilfields and gasfields.

In transport the 'picturesque' days of steam are rapidly passing with the replacement of coal by oil or electricity. One great advantage is that it makes for cleaner travelling, without grit in the eye or smuts on the clothes.

The story of gas was at one time regarded as indissolubly linked with coal but today there are two types of gas—'town' gas and 'natural' gas. Town gas is the one which most of us have known in our homes and it comes from coal being treated in a special way at the gasworks. The coal is baked in sealed ovens, away from the air and, after the gas has been drawn out of the coal, coke is left. But now a new, and it is anticipated, cheaper, form of gas is coming into use—

natural gas. This comes from underground where it has been trapped by impervious rock for thousands of years and is reached by sinking bore-holes or wells. Britain has been importing natural gas from the Sahara and from America and it has now been discovered that there are large quantities of this gas trapped in the earth under the North Sea, on Britain's doorstep. By October 1966 twenty-nine wells had been, or were being, drilled into various areas under the sea and many had started to produce gas.

A minor amount of alteration to gas appliances is necessary when the natural gas is put through the pipes instead of town gas but such changes have already been satisfactorily accomplished in Whitby in Yorkshire and Canvey Island in Essex. The new gas is already being used in Canada, the United States and in several European countries.

The classic story about electricity is that of the student who, being asked, 'What is electricity?', replied, 'I had the answer a moment ago, but it has just slipped from my mind.' 'What a pity!' said the teacher, 'You are the first man to know the answer and now it has escaped you.' And electricity remains a mystery. We know what it does, we know how to produce it, but we do not know what it is. About half the world's electricity is provided by hydro-electric plants where the giant turbines are driven by the pressure of falling water, either at dams or water-falls, but in Great Britain four out of five of our power stations are coal-fired. Solar energy is being developed to produce electricity but this is still in little more than an experimental stage.

Electricity has spread rapidly in this century, one reason being because it is so easy to convey through overhead wires across country. It has become dominant in homes for lighting, competitive in cooking and heating and essential for many of the washing and drying and cleaning machines which are coming in to help housewives. Television and radio would not exist without it.

The last of the heat and power sources we have mentioned, oil, can be said to have started its industrial life when the first oil well was sunk in 1859, but it is one of the very earliest sources of light, using the term oil in the widest sense. Most of us chiefly associate oil with the petrol on which cars, planes and many machines operate, whether as the motive force or for lubrication, but apart from the light obtained from the warming fire, oil provided the earliest light, though it was generally a vegetable or fish oil. Sometimes it wasn't necessary to extract the oil. The sea birds, the stormy petrels are so full of oil that they could be used as lamps merely through the addition of a wick.

In its way the application of fire for the purpose of lighting demonstrates the advance of communities. Where they are isolated, or poor, the oil-lamp still holds sway, though the fuel may now be supplied from the purified product of the oil field.

The coming of gas often meant the first street lighting. In the early days it was not particularly efficient, but it was better than nothing. In the beginning of the eighteen-hundreds it was introduced to London streets, and was also being installed in cotton mills. It was rare enough in 1832 for the town of Lymington, in the south of England, to have a memorial of that date to the introduction of gas lighting of the streets, and to Admiral Sir Harry Neal, for his 'munificent gift of the Iron Columns for the Public Lamps'.

Electric lighting has made tremendous strides in this century because of its safety and convenience, and though the *type* of lamp is now in process of change there is no substitute in sight for electricity in home, office, factory or street lighting, likely to be equally convenient.

This is emphatically not a technical book. If the brief outline of the origin and development of the uses of fire leads to a desire to know more, and to more reading and research, its purpose will have been fulfilled, but a book glancing at the various sources of power is incomplete without a brief reference to atomic discoveries.

When we dealt with the sun we were dealing with an object of such magnitude that figures were difficult to grasp. When we deal with the atom we are trying to convey facts about something so small that the same difficulty arises in reverse. Atoms are so minute that a hundred million placed side by side would measure about an inch, and the small particles which make up the atom, the nucleus and the electron, on the same basis would mean a million million fitting into the same space.

Too much simplification can be dangerously misleading, but if we say that nuclear energy, a more correct term than atomic energy, is the utilization of the heat energy in atoms due to violent agitation we hope nobody will object with a 'but'!

Uranium comes into the picture because it is the heaviest and most complex substance on earth, and its atoms are more unstable and the energy greater than that produced by other elements. Of the various types of uranium ore, Uranium 235 is best for our purpose. Under certain conditions the break-up of particles and release of energy is so great that the whole of the material being dealt with blows apart with such extreme violence as to cause the devastation identified with the atom-bomb.

Control of this catastrophic energy can mean nuclear power of a tremendous potential in solving the energy problems of the world.

Fires of wood, coal, gas, oil or electricity may not be superseded by an atomic or nuclear fire, but the great problem of coping with the demands of industry for more power, greater heat, new materials, may be solved in our time, always supposing somebody doesn't use this same power for greater destruction.

It is estimated that it now costs less per head to kill with the new type bomb than old fashioned warfare. One pound of Uranium 235 has a potential energy equal to that obtained from burning 3,000 tons of coal or a quarter-of-a-million gallons of petrol.

The old fire led men out of the wilderness of prehistoric times. We have to see that the new fire leads forward and doesn't by mishap return us to that wilderness.

Lights in Old London

'*In the months of June and July, on the vigils of festival days, and on the same festival days in the evenings after the sun setting, there were usually made bonfires in the streets, every man bestowing wood or labour towards them; . . . These were called bonfires as well of good amity amongst neighbours that being before at controversy, were there, by the labour of others, reconciled, and made of bitter enemies loving friends; and also for the virtue that a great fire hath to purge the infection of the air. On the vigil of St. John the Baptist, and on St. Peter and Paul the apostles, every man's door . . . had also lamps of glass, with oil burning in them all the night; some hung out branches of iron curiously wrought, containing hundreds of lamps alight at once, which made a goodly show, namely in New Fish street, Thames street, etc. Then had ye besides the standing watches . . . a marching watch, that passed through the principal streets . . . for the furniture whereof with lights, there were appointed seven hundred cressets, five hundred of them being found by the companies, the other two hundred by the chamber of London. Besides the which lights every constable in London, in number more than two hundred and forty, had his cresset: the charge of every cresset was in light two shillings and four pence, and every cresset had two men, one to bear or hold it, another to bear a bag with light, and to serve it. . . .*'

From John Stow's *Survey of London* (1598)

Books for Further Reading

*—Reference books   YP—written for young people

YP *The Battle Again t Fire* by Roy Brown and W. Stuart Thomson	Abelard-Schuman 1966
Beyond the Bounds of History by Henri Breuil	Gawthorn 1949
Bombarded Earth by René Gallant	John Baker 1964
* *Brewer's Dictionary of Phrase and Fable*	Cassell
* *Dictionary of Classical Mythology* by J. E. Zimmerman	Harper & Row 1964
The Elements Rage by Frank W. Lane	David & Charles 1966
Energy by Mitchell Wilson & Editors of *Life*	Time 1965
English Folklore by Christina Hole	Batsford 1945
* *Everyman's Classical Dictionary* by John Warrington	Dent 1961
* *Everyman's Dictionary of Non-Classical Mythology* by Egerton Sykes	Dent 1965
The Fabric of the Heavens by Stephen Toulmin and June Goodfield	Penguin 1963
The Face of the Sun by H. W. Newton	Penguin 1958
Facing the Atomic Future by E. W. Titterton	Macmillan 1956
The Golden Bough by Sir James George Frazer	Macmillan 1922
History of Mankind: Vol. 1 *Prehistory and the Beginnings of Civilization* by Jacquetta Hawkes and Sir Leonard Woolley	UNESCO Allen & Unwin 1963
An Introduction to Cultural Anthropology by Robert H. Lowie	Harrap 1934
Krakatoa by Robert Furneaux	Secker & Warburg 1965
London's Burning by John Bedford	Abelard-Schuman 1966
The Romance of Fire by A. M. Low	Gifford 1941
Science in History by J. D. Bernal	Watts 1965
YP *Science Shapes Tomorrow* by Gerald Leach	Phoenix 1962
* *Dr Smith's Smaller Classical Dictionary*	Murray
Social Life of Early Man ed. by S. L. Washburn ('On man's use of fire' by Kenneth B. Oakley)	Methuen 1962
YP *Solar Energy* by Franklyn M. Branley	Edmund Ward 1959
YP *The Solar System* by Patrick Moore	Methuen 1958
The Sun by Étienne Lalou	Prentice Hall 1963
The Sun and the Amateur Astronomer by W. M. Baxter	Lutterworth 1963

Two Minutes to Noon (The Tokyo-Yokohama Earth-
quake) by Noel F. Busch   Arthur Barker 1963
We Live by the Sun by J. Gordon Cook   Harrap 1957
YP *Volcanoes* by Patricia Lauber   Muller 1966

Index